MW00634369

Cinched

Applying Ten Lessons from Rahab

TO OUR LIVES TODAY

Cinched

Applying Ten Lessons from Rahab
TO OUR LIVES TODAY

COMPANION WORKBOOK

KRISTINE BROWN

Aberdeen
BOOKS LLC

Copyright 2021 by Kristine Brown

Published by Aberdeen Books, LLC, Tyler, Texas

All rights reserved. No part of this publication may be reproduced, distributed, or transmitted in any form or by any means, including photocopying, recording, or other electronic or mechanical methods, without the prior written permission of the publisher, except in the case of brief quotations embodied in critical reviews and certain other noncommercial uses permitted by copyright law. Requests for permission can be addressed to: Permissions, Aberdeen Books, 1910 E SE Loop 323 #231, Tyler, TX, 75701

ISBN: 978-1-7375986-1-9

Scripture quotations marked (NLT) are taken from the Holy Bible, New Living Translation, copyright ©1996, 2004, 2015 by Tyndale House Foundation. Used by permission of Tyndale House Publishers, Carol Stream, Illinois 60188. All rights reserved.

Scripture quotations marked NIV are taken from THE HOLY BIBLE, NEW INTERNATIONAL VERSION®, NIV® Copyright © 1973, 1978, 1984, 2011 by Biblica, Inc.® Used by permission. All rights reserved worldwide.

Scripture quotations marked MSG are taken from The Message. Copyright © 1993, 1994, 1995, 1996, 2000, 2001, 2002. Used by permission of NavPress Publishing Group.

Scripture quotations marked KJV are taken from the King James Bible.

Scripture quotations marked NKJV are taken from the New King James Version®. Copyright © 1982 by Thomas Nelson. Used by permission. All rights reserved.

Scripture quotations are from The ESV® Bible (The Holy Bible, English Standard Version®), copyright © 2001 by Crossway, a publishing ministry of Good News Publishers. Used by permission. All rights reserved.

Scripture quotations taken from the Amplified® Bible (AMP), Copyright © 2015 by The Lockman Foundation. Used by permission. ***www.lockman.org***.

Scripture quotations marked HCSB are taken from the Holman Christian Standard Bible®, Used by Permission HCSB ©1999,2000,2002,2003,2009 Holman Bible Publishers. Holman Christian Standard Bible®, Holman CSB®, and HCSB® are federally registered trademarks of Holman Bible Publishers.

Scripture quotations marked CSB have been taken from the Christian Standard Bible®, Copyright © 2017 by Holman Bible Publishers. Used by permission. Christian Standard Bible® and CSB® are federally registered trademarks of Holman Bible Publishers.

Scripture quotations marked (CEV) are from the Contemporary English Version Copyright © 1991, 1992, 1995 by American Bible Society. Used by Permission.

Cover & Interior Design by: Five J's Design
Editing Services by: Five J's Design

TABLE OF CONTENTS

Ready to Live with Unwavering Trust in a God Who Will Never Fail You?

"If only I could do things differently this time. If only I could ***really*** *trust God in all things."*

These words whispered an unfamiliar hope as I stood at the door of the most difficult trial I'd ever face. Not knowing what waited on the other side, how would I choose to move forward? Was it possible to not only *say* I trusted God but to actively live out that trust in every part of my life?

If you're opening this workbook and thumbing through its pages for the first time, allow me to give you a hearty welcome. I am grateful you're joining me for the adventure. Before we begin, please know this workbook is not designed to stand on its own. If you picked up only this guide, you'll need a copy of *Cinched: Living with Unwavering Trust in an Unfailing God* as well. And I hope you will grab one, because true growth awaits when we commit to take that next faith step.

The *Cinched* book is packed full of Scripture from the story of Rahab, told in the chapters of Joshua, along with many other verses from God's Word. So even though I wanted to provide a study guide to accompany the book, I hesitated. Because the *Cinched* book itself is not only a nonfiction narrative and a Christian living book for women. It is—in essence—a Bible study. The research and various translations used immerse us in Rahab's life along with the lives of other bold women of faith. It is designed to help us strengthen our foundation on biblical truth and inspire us to trust God like we mean it. So, I decided a companion workbook would be just the thing. But what then is the purpose of this companion workbook? If the *Cinched* book has everything the reader needs, why add more?

When God took me on this adventure of

building a new level of trust in Him, I discovered the process was not easy. I needed help. Help sorting through my own struggle with trusting God and applying new habits that would target that struggle. That's why I created this spiritual growth resource. Its purpose is to take the lesson found in each chapter of *Cinched* and work through applying it to our own lives right now, right where we are. Through this life application workbook, we will be given ten challenges that will:

- lead us through a self-assessment of our trust walk.
- help us build on the previous faith lesson.
- turn each *Cinched* Foundation Principle into actionable steps.

To get the most from these pages, I recommend reading the chapter first and then following up with the chapter challenge here. These activities will feel like an extension of what you read in the book and will help seal the message to your heart.

Need to pause and get a copy of *Cinched: Living with Unwavering Trust in an Unfailing God?* You'll find everything you need to know about the *Cinched* book along with other trust-building resources at ***Cinchedbook.com.*** Now that we're ready to learn how to trust God like we mean it, let's get started, soul-sister.

CHALLENGE #1

Preparing to Weave a New Cord

TRUSTING GOD LIKE WE MEAN IT

FOUNDATION PRINCIPLE

Moving to a new level of trust begins with knowing real change is possible and acknowledging we need help getting there.

With the first foundation principle in mind, let's take a few moments to complete the first challenge.

KEY VERSES

- 1 Peter 5:7
- Philippians 4:6-7
- John 14:27
- Psalm 112:7
- Ephesians 4:29
- Ecclesiastes 4:12
- Romans 15:13

THOUGHT PROMPT

I had expended all my energy "trying to stay positive." I didn't realize how exhausted I was from that cycle until I hit a wall. I had nothing left. That's when God showed me that I could choose a better way. I may have been starting the biggest trial of my life, but this time could truly be different—a life-changing kind of difference. Whether or not to take that first step of the journey was up to me.

Although I hadn't shared publicly about my diagnosis, a friend who knew about the cancer began sending texts every day. Little messages: sometimes a simple heart emoji or a link to an inspirational song. I noticed how those acts of care strengthened my resolve and became an integral part of my battle strategy. Our hearts intertwined. I sensed the Holy Spirit replacing the energy and strength I'd spent so I could start anew.

THE RAHAB CONNECTION: In Rahab's day, women would often weave fine linen to create cord. In the same way, God weaves us together with other women to create one beautiful story. In what areas of your life do you need the support of other women through prayer or encouragement?

APPLYING IT

1. **In what areas of my life do I struggle to trust God?** *(Check all that apply.)*

- ☐ Health
- ☐ Finances
- ☐ Children
- ☐ Marriage
- ☐ Parents
- ☐ Romantic relationships
- ☐ Ministry
- ☐ Job opportunities
- ☐ Big challenges
- ☐ Daily decisions
- ☐ The future
- ☐ All of the above!
- ☐ Other: ___________________________

2. **I know when I struggle to trust God, it causes ______.** *(Check all that apply.)*

- ☐ Defeat
- ☐ Frustration
- ☐ Worry
- ☐ Stress
- ☐ Feeling like a failure
- ☐ Feeling stuck
- ☐ Guilt
- ☐ Doubt
- ☐ Panic
- ☐ Sleeplessness
- ☐ All of the above!
- ☐ Other: ___________________________

3. **When I learn to fully trust God, the real result will be ______.** *(Check all that apply.)*

- ☐ Peace
- ☐ Victorious living
- ☐ Joy
- ☐ Freedom
- ☐ Contentment
- ☐ Calm
- ☐ Discovering my purpose
- ☐ Confidence
- ☐ Steadfastness
- ☐ Rest
- ☐ All of the above!
- ☐ Other: ___________________________

CHALLENGE #2

Shutting the Gate on Worry

WHEN MY PROBLEM KEEPS ME UP AT NIGHT.

FOUNDATION PRINCIPLE

Remember the foundation principle we learned in Chapter 2?

By daily releasing control to God, we trust His peace to calm the decision-making chaos.

Let's focus on the foundation principle as we answer the questions below.

KEY VERSES

- Psalm 31:14
- Joshua 2:1-7
- Numbers 14:14
- Psalm 55:22
- 1 Corinthians 14:33
- Deuteronomy 31:6

THOUGHT PROMPT

THE RAHAB CONNECTION: Rahab's decisive obedience activated the plan. Once the gate shut, there was no turning back. She had to trust God. Take a moment to think of an area where you are having a hard time trusting God. Is it time to close the gate, or are you in a time of waiting and seeking God more?

APPLYING IT

1. What types of decisions do you struggle with the most? *(Check all that apply.)*

- ☐ My health
- ☐ Education or health decisions for my kids
- ☐ For my aging parents
- ☐ Boundaries in my life
- ☐ Financial decisions
- ☐ Reactive decisions related to world events/disasters
- ☐ Job-related decisions
- ☐ Relationships
- ☐ Other: ______________________

2. Do you often wonder if you heard God right? Or if God answered you at all?

Let's review the prayer for peace from the end of Chapter 2. It will help us sense His peace and trust that He is with us as our Helper, even when we don't feel or hear Him:

Dear Heavenly Father,

It's easy to get caught up in the craziness of daily life and forget about your loving presence. You are here with me, but distractions take my attention away from the Holy Spirit, who offers peace and calm in the midst of the chaos. Lord, in those times when decisions overwhelm me, help me stay aware of your presence. I know you will never leave me nor forsake me (Deuteronomy 31:6 NIV).

I know I can stay connected with you by offering short, simple prayers anytime. Words like, "Lord, I need you" or "I give you praise" will redirect my thoughts toward you and help me be aware of your leading. Lord, guide me along your path. When I have you, I don't need anything else. Thank you for the gift of your calming presence in my life. In Jesus' name, Amen.

3. Have you ever stayed awake at night or had trouble resting due to second-guessing whether you made the right decision? Jot your thoughts on the lines below.

____

____

____

____

____

4. Write this verse in a journal or notecard and keep it close to your bed. Read it when your decisions interrupt your sleep.

"The steadfast love of the Lord never ceases; his mercies never come to an end; they are new every morning; great is your faithfulness" (Lamentations 3:22-23 ESV).

For a printable list of Scriptures for winning the battle over worry, visit this link:

https://bit.ly/3AAprOe

We will explore waiting in more detail in Chapter 8.

CHALLENGE #3

Building a Strong Shelter of Trust

I know God is real. So why does my mind keep imagining the worst?

FOUNDATION PRINCIPLE

In our third challenge, we will work through a quiz in order to determine which level of trust we identify with the most at this time in our lives. Then at the end of the quiz, we will find a verse that will help us continue building on the foundation principle from the chapter:

We build a strong shelter of trust in God when we move from knowing, to saying, to doing.

KEY VERSES

- Hebrews 10:23
- Romans 8:1
- Joshua 2:8-13
- Isaiah 26:4
- Ephesians 3:20
- Psalm 46:1

THOUGHT PROMPT

THE RAHAB CONNECTION: Rahab gathered intel then expressed her belief in knowing who God is through her words and actions. If someone asked you today, "Who is God?" How would you answer that question? What is one memory you hold onto to remind you of God's faithfulness?

APPLYING IT

THE TRUST LEVEL QUIZ

Answer each question in the quiz by circling the answer that best describes you right now. Try to answer honestly. If a question doesn't apply to you (like a parenting question), you may skip it. Answer without thinking too long about your choice.

1. When I have a big decision to make, this is what I usually do first:

A. Find someone I trust to talk to about it, like a spouse or friend.

B. Pray about it, then think about all the possible outcomes.

C. Pray about it and give it to God.

2. When I'm in a frustrating situation, the first thing I usually do is ______.

A. Get upset, and maybe call a friend to vent.

B. Ask someone to pray for me.

C. Look up a helpful verse or pray and ask God for help.

3. When my child makes a wrong choice, I ______.

A. Wonder what I did wrong as a parent.

B. Pray and then figure out ways to help him/her understand the mistake.

C. Pray that the lesson will help him/her grow spiritually, then move on.

4. When a new opportunity is in front of me, I ______.

A. Make a list of the pros and cons, then get frustrated when I still can't decide.

B. Figure out how this opportunity will affect everyone else in my life.

C. Don't make a move until I hear clear direction from God.

5. When I pray and don't hear an answer from God, I mostly feel ______.

A. Frantic.

B. Eager.

C. Calm.

6. When I'm facing a big problem, this best describes me:

A. Grumpy Gertie.

B. Over-analyzing Annie.

C. Positive Patty.

7. When my kids or other loved ones face a problem, this best describes me:

A. Guilty Gabby.

B. Intervening Ida.

C. Hopeful Haddie.

8. When I'm unsure or afraid, this is what I do:

A. Panic, then make a plan.

B. Pray, then pace with uncertainty.

C. Pray, then proceed with confidence.

9. This best describes my sleep pattern:

A. What pattern? It's all over the place.

B. I sleep pretty well, but problems tend to keep me awake.

C. I give my problems to God then catch some Zs.

10. This best describes my relationship with God at this time:

A. I know God is real but haven't felt close to Him in a while.

B. I like spending time with God and reading the Bible when I can.

C. I talk to God all throughout the day.

HOW TO SCORE THE QUIZ

Count the number of A's, B's, and C's, and record those numbers in the blanks here:

A	B	C
______	______	______

If your highest number is in the A column, you identify most with the ***Knowledge Level*** of trust in God. Here is your personal verse for this week. Let it encourage you as you strengthen your trust in our Heavenly Father.

"Don't be afraid, for I am with you. Don't be discouraged, for I am your God. I will strengthen you and help you. I will hold you up with my victorious right hand" (Isaiah 41:10 NLT).

If your highest number is in the B column, you identify most with the ***Verbal Level*** of trust in God. Here is your personal verse for this week. Let it encourage you as you strengthen your trust in our Heavenly Father.

"Don't worry about anything; instead, pray about everything. Tell God what you need, and thank him for all he has done. Then you will experience God's peace, which exceeds anything we can understand..." (Philippians 4:6-7 NLT).

If your highest number is in the C column, you identify most with the ***Active Level*** of trust in God. Here is your personal verse for this week. Let it encourage you as you strengthen your trust in our Heavenly Father.

"Teach me to do your will, for you are my God. May your gracious Spirit lead me forward on a firm footing" (Psalm 143:10 NLT).

As we draw closer to Jesus, we will learn to trust from a secure dwelling place. We will learn to trust God without wavering!

CHALLENGE #4

Input Overload

THE IMPORTANCE OF CREATING QUIET AMID ALL THE NOISE.

FOUNDATION PRINCIPLE

Look again at the foundation principle we discovered in Chapter 4.

When we trust God amid all the noise, confusion clears away, revealing His truth for my trial.

Highlight, circle, or underline three words that stand out to you in that sentence.

KEY VERSES

- Proverbs 29:25
- Philippians 4:8
- John 17:17
- 2 Kings 4:1-6
- Psalm 40:4

THOUGHT PROMPT

THE RAHAB CONNECTION: In Rahab's town, word spread fast about the spies. Bad news can send our minds spinning, causing confusion. In what ways can you "focus your thoughts" the next time you receive bad news?

APPLYING IT

In Philippians 4:8, Paul tells us to "fix our thoughts on what is true." Let's take a moment to prayerfully consider what is distracting us from fixing our minds on God's truth about our circumstances. No judgment here, only freedom that comes from honestly opening our hearts to God's restoring ways.

1. **I let ____________ overwhelm my thoughts and distract me from what is true.** *(Check all that apply.)*

   - ☐ Too much information
   - ☐ The need to be informed
   - ☐ Pleasing others
   - ☐ Seeking advice or opinions
   - ☐ Making assumptions
   - ☐ Wanting to be right
   - ☐ Other: ________________________

When distractions overwhelm us in the midst of seeking truth, we cannot discern what is best for us and our situation. God's Word says in 1 Corinthians 14:33a, "For God is not a God of confusion but of peace" (ESV). So we can rest assured that any confusion is not from God. That's great news for us today! Whatever other 'news' comes our way, we can breathe a sigh of relief. We will sense the Holy Spirit guiding us in peace and certainty as we focus our thoughts on God's Truth.

Ready to clear away some confusion and allow God to begin renewing your mind? There's a section in the back of *Cinched* I created just for you. It's called the "Glossary of God's Promises." Flip over to that glossary now and skim through the verses. When one reaches out and grabs hold of you, write it on the lines here. This is a verse of truth for you today.

2. **A verse of truth I can focus on right now:**

____

____

____

____

____

If you're studying with a friend, discuss your answers. Sharing ideas helps us grow stronger. If you are working through this study on your own, I'm proud of you for taking this faith step!

CHALLENGE #5

The Power in the Promise

I PRAYED, SO WHY DO I KEEP OVERANALYZING ALL THE POSSIBLE OUTCOMES?

FOUNDATION PRINCIPLE

Here's a refresher of the Chapter 5 foundation principle.

Free yourself from the tangle of all the possible outcomes. Cinch your trust as tight as you can to God's guarantee.

KEY VERSES

- Psalm 12:6
- Psalm 37:3
- Joshua 2:14-21
- Colossians 4:6
- John 1:17
- James 2:25
- Luke 12:7
- John 11:1-3 & 32
- Psalm 119:105

THOUGHT PROMPT

In Chapter 5, we learned the big moment in Rahab's story— the turning point for her and for our lives as well. We must cinch our trust to God's promise, no matter what. Rahab's scarlet cord represented a binding oath. She would secure her trust to God's guarantee, whatever the outcome.

THE RAHAB CONNECTION: What "tiqvah," or outcome, do you need to trust God with today? In what area of your life have you been reluctant to cinch your trust to God's guarantee?

Whatever your response to the question in The Rahab Connection, freedom awaits as you release the need-to-know and rest in the truth that your struggle could be part of God's bigger plan for your life. Write the chapter foundation principle on a sticky note and place it where you're sure to see it every day this week. Repeat it aloud as you experience renewed faith in God's powerful promises.

APPLYING IT

I jotted down this quote from my friend Lyli Dunbar's post "Strength to Stick it Out" on her website, LyliDunbar.com. Let's read it silently and see what it evokes in us.

"My mighty God is Lord over all. He is my Refuge and Shield. The Lord will protect me from pandemics and has promised me a heavenly home. He is the God of Angel Armies. He will command His warrior angels to guard my loves in all their ways. He is my Provider. His storehouse supply is abundant. He sees my need and will sustain me. He is a Present Help. He will never leave me nor forsake me. I do not walk alone."

Praise God! Doesn't it revive your spirit reading those words? Now try reading them out loud and see what these promises will do! When our confidence fades due to uncertainties we face, we find the power we need in the promises of God. What other promises could you add to the list above?

CHALLENGE #6

Trading What-Ifs for Living As-If

HOW DO I IDENTIFY MY PROMISE?

FOUNDATION PRINCIPLE

Spend a few minutes sealing this chapter foundation principle on your heart:

I can leave what-ifs behind and live as-if God's Word is true, because it is.

KEY VERSES

- Deuteronomy 7:9
- Mark 9:23
- Psalm 23:4
- Numbers 14:10
- Numbers 14:17

THOUGHT PROMPT

THE RAHAB CONNECTION: Rahab's promise came right when she needed it, although it likely didn't look the way she expected. Our answers from God often will be more than our human minds can comprehend. That's why immersing ourselves in His Word and studying His truth for our lives will help us see the answer when it comes knocking at our door.

APPLYING IT

1. **Once we've tied our knot in place, what-if questions may work their way into our newfound commitment to trusting God.**

We have a tendency to entertain what-if questions instead of living as-if God's promise is sealed in place. List of few what-if questions from your own journey either here or on the next page.

2. **How can you trade the what-ifs listed with living as-if God's Word is true?**

Using the chart in Chapter 6 or the space here in the workbook on the next page, reword the what-if questions into as-if statements of truth. If you're going through this study with a friend or group, help each other identify ways to live as-if.

3. **Sometimes we unknowingly open our minds to what-ifs because we get in a rut in our Bible study or prayer life.**

Finding new ways to connect with Jesus can revitalize our spirits. Here are a few creative ways to refresh our time with the Lord. Which of these appeal to your personality? Scribble down any additional ideas you'd like to try.

CREATIVE WAYS TO REFRESH YOUR TIME WITH GOD

- ☐ Journaling in your Bible
- ☐ Using a coloring Bible to create Scripture art
- ☐ Choosing a new worship song to play while praying or praising God
- ☐ Inviting the presence of the Holy Spirit into your life
- ☐ Taking a walk in nature, praising God as you appreciate His creation
- ☐ Writing a poem or song expressing your prayers

4. **Which of the above ideas would you like to try? Do any of these inspire other ideas for you?**

CHALLENGE #7

Leaving the Knot Alone

HOW DO I RESIST HELPING GOD? WHEN WAITING ON THE PROMISE LEADS TO DOUBT.

FOUNDATION PRINCIPLE

Let's begin by reviewing the truth of foundation principle #7:

Don't let your faith wane in the waiting. Keep trusting.

KEY VERSES

- Psalm 9:10
- Psalm 130:5
- Joshua 2:21b-24
- Joshua 3:5
- Hosea 6:3
- Joshua 4:19
- Isaiah 40:31
- Joshua 6:16-17

THOUGHT PROMPT

THE RAHAB CONNECTION: Once Rahab sent the spies away through her window, she had quite the wait ahead of her. What can we learn from looking at all that happened while Rahab waited? How does Rahab's story of obedience encourage us to wait well?

APPLYING IT

1. **What do you struggle with most while waiting on God to answer your prayer or work in your situation?** *(Check all that apply.)*

- ☐ Resisting helping God
- ☐ Frustration
- ☐ Doubt
- ☐ Unbelief
- ☐ Defeated thinking
- ☐ Complaining
- ☐ Other: ____________________

2. **Do you recall a time of waiting in your own life? A time when you wanted to help God?**

Maybe you're in a waiting season right now. If so, let our foundation principle settle into your heart. *Don't let your faith wane in the waiting. Keep trusting.* Seal the words of our foundation principle by typing them into a notes app on your phone or speaking them into the voice recorder app. Now think of a friend who needs to hear this encouragement today. Before you turn another page, text it to that friend and see how she responds.

CHALLENGE #8

Decision Stages

MAYBE THIS WASN'T SUCH A GOOD IDEA!

FOUNDATIONAL PRINCIPAL

The eighth foundation principle from Rahab's life is this:

If we've asked the Holy Spirit to guide us, we need to trust that He's doing it.

Take a moment to reflect on that idea before moving forward with the chapter challenge below.

KEY VERSES

- Proverbs 3:5-6
- Psalm 62:8
- Psalm 73:24
- Psalm 84:12
- Psalm 32:8
- Isaiah 30:21

THOUGHT PROMPT

THE RAHAB CONNECTION: With roads diverging before her in every direction, Rahab chose the one that held the promise. Think of a time in your life when you experienced panic, regret, or guilt over a decision you made. Or maybe you reversed your decision because you questioned whether you heard God right. Take time right now to talk to God about that experience. What do you sense Him saying to you? Let God's love, patience, and forgiveness flow into your heart and refresh you right now. He is with you. Trust in that.

APPLYING IT

1. **In the space provided below, jot down everything you can remember about the Holy Spirit.**

Take as much time as you need. If you would like help, feel free to use your favorite search tool on your computer, app on your phone, or Bible concordance to do a quick Scripture reference search.

2. **After reading over all you discovered about the Holy Spirit, how do you feel about His role in our lives as women of faith?**

Let's pause for a moment and invite the Holy Spirit to be present with us right now. Let's pray and ask God for a deeper, stronger connection with His Spirit, who is at work in us and through us.

CHALLENGE #9

When Your World Is Crumbling Around You

WILL THINGS EVER GET BETTER?

FOUNDATION PRINCIPLE

In our journey through Rahab's story, we discovered foundation principle 9 when her world seemed to be falling apart:

We can be deceived by our crumbling circumstances unless we've built our foundation on trusting God.

KEY VERSES

- Psalm 16:8
- James 1:2-3
- Joshua 6:20-25
- Psalm 95:4-5
- Isaiah 42:5
- 2 Corinthians 5:7
- Psalm 75:3

THOUGHT PROMPT

THE RAHAB CONNECTION: Through Rahab's story, we learned that the answer or promise often comes in the middle of a difficult circumstance, not once the rubble is cleared away. It's hard to keep holding onto God's promises when our worlds seem to be falling apart, but that's where we develop our trust muscles.

APPLYING IT

In Chapter 9 of *Cinched,* I share how God used 2 Corinthians 5:7 to reassure me of His plan for me in a time of waiting in my own cancer battle.

1. **In what area of your life have you needed to live by believing God's Word instead of your circumstances?**

Was there a time when you looked around and only saw hopelessness, which was in contrast to God's Word?

2. **As you pray, what is one verse God brings to mind that you can apply to your current circumstances?**

Do you have a go-to verse to help you through difficult times? Use the Glossary of God's Promises in the back of the *Cinched* book to find a verse that speaks to your heart in a special way today.

CHALLENGE #10

Standing Firm in the River of Daily Demands

How to not get swept away when the current starts rushing again.

FOUNDATION PRINCIPLE

Our final foundation principle can be found in Chapter 10:

When life brings a rush of challenges, we can still overflow with hope by keeping God at the center.

Give yourself a moment to reflect on this principle before moving to the thought prompt below.

KEY VERSES

- Romans 15:13
- Joshua 3:11-16
- Joshua 4:10
- Chronicles 29:11
- Joshua 4:18
- Psalm 16:11
- Jeremiah 17:7
- Matthew 1:5-6
- Psalm 33:4
- 1 Peter 4:19

THOUGHT PROMPT

In the book of Joshua Chapter 4, God directed Joshua to send the priests into the Jordan River ahead of the people, carrying the Ark of the Covenant. As long as they held the Ark in the center, the waters stayed back. Once the Israelites crossed safely, the waters would flow again.

THE RAHAB CONNECTION: As Rahab waited in her home, a miracle happened on the banks of the Jordan River. God kept the waters away while the Israelites crossed into their promised inheritance.

A raging current can throw us off balance, but keeping God at the center will help us when waters rage. Now that you've moved to a new level of trust in God, what daily demands threaten to pull your feet out from under you? How can you keep God placed firmly in the center of your life?

APPLYING IT

1. Take a look at the New Living Translation version of Romans 15:13.

You'll find it at the beginning of Chapter 10, right under the title. Write out that verse here, then circle or highlight any keywords that stand out to you:

____

____

____

____

____

____

2. Read the above verse out loud, then answer these next two questions thoughtfully and prayerfully:

After reading ***Cinched***, in what areas of my life am I trusting God more? *(Check all that apply.)*

- ☐ Health
- ☐ Finances
- ☐ Children
- ☐ Marriage
- ☐ Parents
- ☐ Romantic relationships
- ☐ Ministry
- ☐ Job opportunities
- ☐ Big challenges
- ☐ Daily decisions
- ☐ The future
- ☐ All of the above!
- ☐ Other: ________________________

Which of these do I feel like I'm experiencing more? *(Check all that apply.)*

- ☐ Peace
- ☐ Victorious living
- ☐ Joy
- ☐ Freedom
- ☐ Contentment
- ☐ Calm
- ☐ Discovering my purpose
- ☐ Confidence
- ☐ Steadfastness
- ☐ Rest
- ☐ All of the above!
- ☐ Other: ________________________

3. Write a prayer for yourself on the next page to remind you of your newfound trust in God.

For examples, see the Untying Old Habits prayers at the end of Chapters 1-9 in the book.

My Prayer for Trusting God

About the Author

Kristine Brown is a communicator at heart, nurturer by God's design, and life-long learner and teacher. She is a wife, mom, stepmom, and Mimi.

Kristine and her husband have endured challenges like infertility, long-distance family relationships, life-threatening illness, and life in ministry. Through it all, Kristine has seen God's faithfulness and felt His unfailing love. One of her favorite things is connecting women today with women of the Bible through our shared experiences.

Kristine is a contributing writer for iBelieve.com, Crosswalk.com, Unlocked for Teens devotions, and more. You'll also find her work published on P31's Encouragement for Today, Christianity Today, and (in)Courage. Kristine and her husband Phil live in Texas.

To connect with Kristine or learn more about her other books and resources, visit her online home, ***www.kristinebrown.net.***

Made in the USA
Columbia, SC
10 August 2022

65031136R00030